C000115601

Key Stage 2

Statistics

Hilary Koll and Steve Mills

Name _____

Schofield & Sims

We use statistics every day to help us collect, organise and understand information (data). Knowledge of statistics allows you to do many things, such as predict the weather, prepare for emergencies and develop medicines. In this book you will learn how to draw and interpret different types of graphs, including pictograms, Carroll diagrams and scatter graphs. You will also practise finding the mean, median, mode and range of a set of data.

How to use this book

Before you start using this book, write your name in the name box on the first page.

Then decide how to begin. If you want a complete course on statistics, you should work right through the book from beginning to end. Another way to use the book is to dip into it when you want to find out about a particular topic, such as Venn diagrams. The Contents page will help you to find the pages you need.

Whichever way you choose, don't try to do too much at once – it's better to work through the book in short bursts.

When you have found the topic you want to study, look out for the icons below which mark different parts of the text.

This icon shows you the activities that you should complete. You write your answers in the spaces provided. You might find it useful to have some spare paper to work on for some of the activities. After you have worked through all the activities on the page, turn to pages 45–49 at the end of the book to check your answers. When you are sure that you understand the topic, put a tick in the box beside it on the Contents page.

On pages 11, 20, 28 and 38 you will find **Progress tests**. These contain questions that will check your understanding of the topics that you have worked through so far. Check your answers on page 50. It is important that you correct any mistakes before moving on to the next section.

On pages 41–44 you will find a **Final test**. This will check your understanding of all the topics. Check your answers on page 51.

Explanation

This text explains the topic and gives examples. Make sure you read it before you start the activities.

This text gives you useful background information about the subject.

Contents

Lists

Explanation

Data is information about something. It can be in:

words   (a list of actors in a film)

numbers   (football league table)

pictures   (drawings of birds that visit your garden).

Data can also be organised into **lists**, **tables**, **diagrams**, **charts** and **graphs**.

Example

Here is a list of things to buy from the greengrocers.

Item	Number
bananas	6
apples	8
oranges	4
onions	2
tomatoes	5

Activities

1   Make lists under the headings below.

a

The names of your five favourite TV programmes

_____

_____

_____

_____

b

Five boys' names that begin with the letter B

_____

_____

_____

_____

2   Make a list of all the even numbers between **9** and **25**.

_____

Pictograms 1

Explanation

You can show information on a pictogram, which uses pictures and symbols, as below.

Example

Pictogram of the favourite crisps of children of Class 4					Pictogram of the pets of children in Class 4						
ready salted	☺	☺	☺	☺	hamster	□	□	□			
cheese and onion	☺	☺			cat	□	□	□	□	□	
salt and vinegar	☺	☺	☺	☺ ☺	dog	□	□	□	□	□	□
chicken	☺	☺	☺		rabbit	□	□				

☺ = **1** person   □ = **1** person

You can see that **3** people chose chicken crisps and **6** children have a dog.

Activities

1 Count each type of fruit. Draw a pictogram to show this, using ◯ = **1** piece of fruit.

Pictogram of different types of fruit

 bananas   ◯

 apples

 pears

 oranges

 pineapples

 strawberries

Pictograms 2

Explanation

The pictures used in a pictogram can stand for more than one item. In this pictogram, ▲ stands for **2** coins.

Example

Coins in my pocket

The pictogram shows that I have:
eight 1p coins,
five 2p coins,
four 5p coins,
no 10p coins and
three 50p coins in my pocket.

Activities

1 Look at this pictogram, and answer the questions. Each ★ stands for **2** children.

The bedtimes of children in Class 2

7.00 p.m.	★
7.30 p.m.	★ ★ ⋆
8.00 p.m.	★ ★ ★ ★
8.30 p.m.	★ ★
9.00 p.m.	⋆

a How many children go to bed at **7.30** p.m.? _____

b How many children are in bed by **8.05** p.m.? _____

c How many more children go to bed at **7.30** p.m. than at **8.30** p.m.? _____

d How many children are in the class altogether? _____

2 Draw a pictogram of this data, where ■ stands for **10** people.

Number of people in the shop at these times	
Time	**Number of people**
10 a.m.	10
12 noon	20
2 p.m.	0
4 p.m.	15
6 p.m.	35

People in the shop

10 a.m.	
12 noon	
2 p.m.	
4 p.m.	
6 p.m.	

Frequency tables

A **frequency table** is a way of recording how often something happens or how many of certain things there are. You might make a frequency table of the number of goals scored in the Premiership or the makes of cars in the car park.

Example

Make of car	Number in car park
Ford	2
Nissan	4
Mazda	1
Vauxhall	5
Rover	2

Activities

1   A lot of pets live in this house. Count them, make a frequency table of the data, and answer the questions.

Pet		Number
	hamsters	
	dogs	
	cats	
	rabbits	
	budgies	

a How many dogs are there? _____

b Which pet are there two of? _____

c Which two pets together make a total of 9?

_____ and _____

d How many pets are in the house altogether? _____

e How many more hamsters than cats are there? _____

Tallying

Explanation

On page 7 you learnt that a frequency table shows how often something happens or how many things there are. To make a frequency table you can use **tallying**. This lets you record data very quickly because you just make a single mark for each thing, like cars passing the school or birds on the bird table.

To make the tallies easy to count, they are grouped in fives. The fifth mark goes across the other tallies to group them together, like this ⤸₩₩ = **5**.

You can then write the **frequency** (or total) alongside.

These tables are also known as **tally charts**.

Example

A tally chart showing how many birds visited the bird table in 1 hour

Type	Tally	Frequency
blackbird	₩₩	5
robin	||	2
sparrow	₩₩ ||	7
magpie	||||	4
greenfinch	₩₩ ₩₩ |	11

Activities

1 Roll a dice 50 times. Use tallies to record your results. When you have finished, write the frequency (that is, the number of times that number was rolled altogether) alongside.

Dice number	Tally	Frequency
1		
2		
3		
4		
5		
6		

2 Which number did you roll most often? _____

Drawing bar charts 1

Explanation

Bar charts, like other graphs, show information (or data) as a picture to make it more easily understood. This bar chart has a **vertical axis** showing **frequency**, marked 0 to 10, and a **horizontal axis** showing the types of birds that visited the bird table. When you are drawing bar charts, always label each axis and give your graph a **title**.

Example

A bar graph showing how many of each type of bird visited the bird table in 1 hour

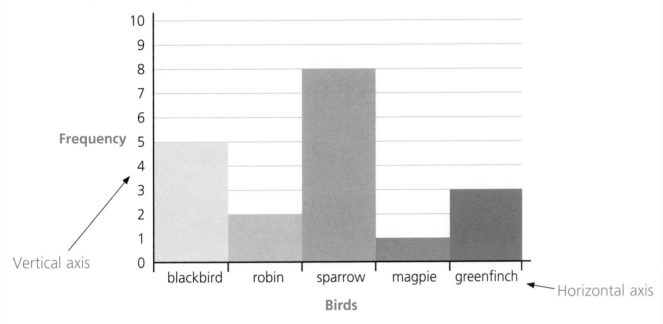

The plural of axis is 'axes', pronounced 'axees', so we say the bar chart has two axes.

Activities

1   During the week, Jennie counts the number of biscuits eaten by her dog, Buster.
    Draw a bar chart using the data in this frequency table.

Day	Number of biscuits
Mon	7
Tue	10
Wed	0
Thu	8
Fri	6
Sat	3
Sun	9

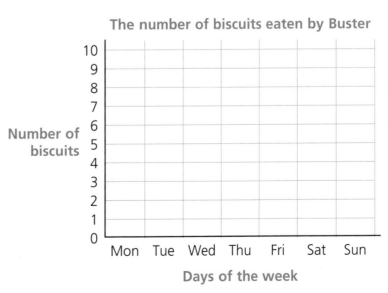

Drawing bar charts 2

Activities

1 Draw a bar chart using the data in this frequency table. Don't forget to label the axes.

Coins in my money box

Coins	Number of coins
1p	15
2p	20
5p	10
10p	5
20p	25
50p	10
£1	5

Coins in my money box

2 Draw a bar chart using the data in this frequency table. Put the spinner number along the horizontal axis and the number of times each number lands (frequency) on the vertical axis.

Results of spinning a spinner

Spinner number	Number of times spun
1	6
2	10
3	9
4	8
5	7
6	10

Results of spinning a spinner

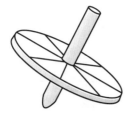

Progress test 1

1 Make a list of all the multiples of **5** between **7** and **47**.

_____

2 Look at this pictogram, and answer the questions. Each ● stands for **2** units.

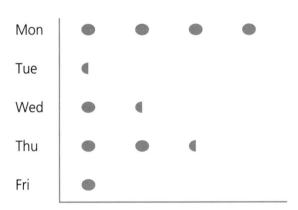

Merits given by our teacher this week

a How many merits were
   given on Monday?   _____

b How many merits were
   given on Tuesday?   _____

c On which day did the
   teacher give three merits? _____

d How many merits were
   given altogether?   _____

3 Fill in the frequencies in this tally chart and draw a bar chart using the data.

Ride	The number of times I went on	
	Tally	**Frequency**
Twister	III	
Laser	++++	
Cascade	II	
Screamer	++++ III	
Warp	++++ I	

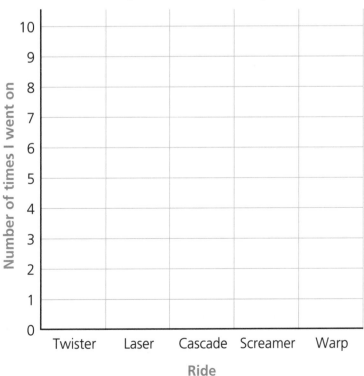

My visit to the theme park

Number of times I went on

10 9 8 7 6 5 4 3 2 1 0

Twister Laser Cascade Screamer Warp

Ride

Reading scales

Explanation

The scales on axes on bar charts and other graphs can be numbered in different ways. Usually the numbers on the vertical axis (the one going up) start at zero and go up in equal steps, such as in **1**s, **2**s, **5**s, **10**s, **20**s, **50**s, **100**s and so on.

Not every interval is numbered so you must learn to work out the values of these or to estimate the value of any position on the scale.

Example

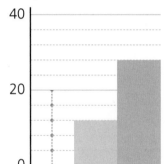

This scale is numbered in **20**s. There are **5** intervals for each **20**. Divide to find out the value of each interval.
20 ÷ 5 = 4 so each interval is worth **4**.

To work out the value for the first bar, count on in **4**s from **0**.
Its value is **12**.

To work out the value for the second bar, count on in **4**s from **20**.
Its value is **28**.

Activities

1   Write the value for each bar on these scales.

a
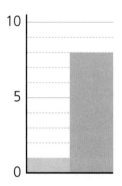

____ ____

b
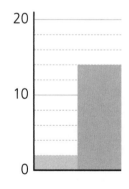

____ ____

c
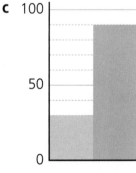

____ ____

d
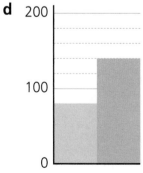

____ ____

e
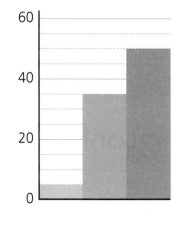

____ ____ ____

f
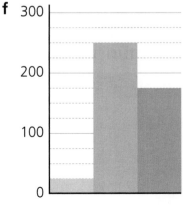

____ ____ ____

Interpreting bar charts 1

These bar charts show the number of visits to the library over a two-week period.

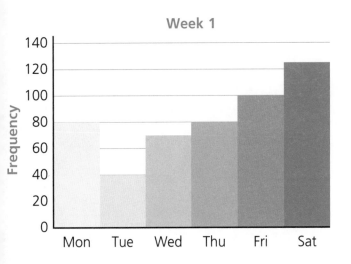

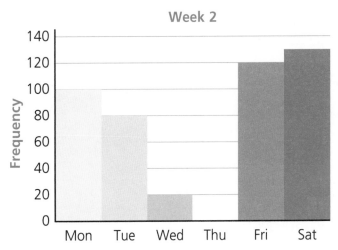

Activities

1   In week **1**, about how many people visited the library on:

   a Monday? _____   **b** Wednesday? _____   **c** Saturday? _____

2   In week **2**, about how many people visited the library on:

   a Monday? _____   **b** Wednesday? _____   **c** Saturday? _____

3   On which day in week **1** were there about **70** visitors? _____

4   What might have happened on Thursday of week **2**?

   _____

5   Why might more people visit the library on Saturdays?

   _____

6   Which day in week **2** had the same number of visitors as Monday of week **1**? _____

Venn diagrams

Venn diagrams show information by using circles inside a rectangle. The rectangle contains all the data and each circle shows a part of the data (a **set**) that is related in some way. Sometimes the circles overlap, showing that some things belong in more than one set.

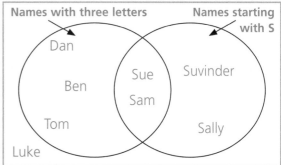

Did you know?

Venn diagrams were named after John Venn who was a mathematician at Cambridge University in the 1800s.

Example

This Venn diagram shows how the numbers between **1** and **10** were sorted.

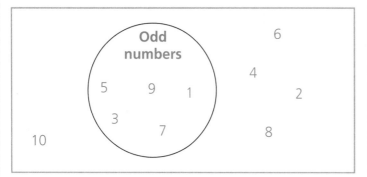

The odd numbers are in a circle and the even numbers are outside the circle.

The Venn diagram shows how some names were sorted.

The names with three letters are in one set and the names starting with S are in another. The three-letter names beginning with S belong in both sets, so they go in the middle.

Activities

1 Sort these numbers using this Venn diagram.

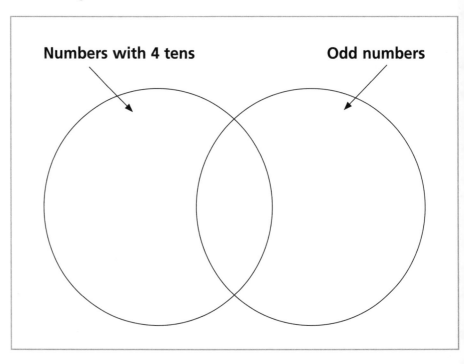

47	35
26	14
48	30
41	27
44	25
40	19

Think carefully about where numbers like 26, 30 and 14 will go.

Carroll diagrams

Explanation

Carroll diagrams show information using rows and columns.

Did you know?

Carroll diagrams were named after Lewis Carroll who wrote Alice in Wonderland.

Example

This Carroll diagram shows how the numbers between **1** and **10** were sorted.

Odd	Not odd
1	2
3	4
5	6
7	8
9	10

If one column is 'odd' then the other is the opposite, so it is called 'not odd'.

This Carroll diagram shows how some names were sorted.

	Names that start with S	Names that do not start with S
Names that have three letters	Sue Sam	Ben Dan Tom
Names that do not have three letters	Suvinder Sally	Luke

Take each name and find which column it belongs in. Then find which row it belongs in.

Activities

1 Sort these numbers using this Carroll diagram.

47   35
26   14
48   30
41   27
44   25
40   19

Take each number and find which column it belongs in. Then find which row it belongs in.

	Odd	Not odd
Numbers that have four 10s	41	
Numbers that do not have four 10s		

Interpreting bar charts 2

Bar charts are sometimes shown with the frequency along the horizontal axis.

This graph shows the number of cousins some children have.

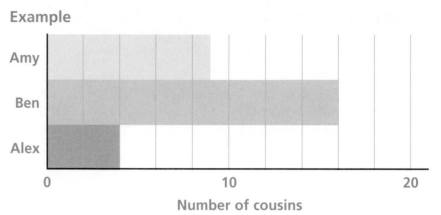

Example

The bar chart shows that Amy has **9** cousins, Ben has **16** cousins and Alex has **4** cousins.

Activities

1 In a sports day competition, children collect as many beanbags as they can. This graph shows the number of beanbags collected by each child.

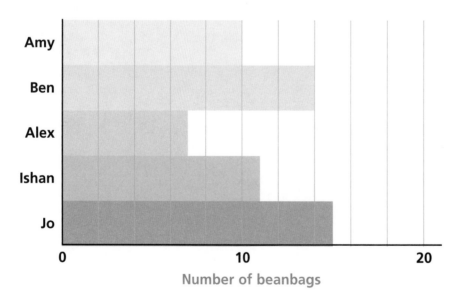

Number of beanbags

How many beanbags were collected by:

a Alex? _____

b Ben? _____

c Amy? _____

d Jo? _____

e Ishan? _____

2 How many more beanbags did:

a Ben collect than Alex? _____

b Amy collect than Alex? _____

3 How many beanbags did Jo and Amy collect altogether? _____

4 What was the total number of beanbags collected by all the children? _____

Statistics

Grouped data

Explanation

When collecting data, it can sometimes make more sense to group data to make it easier to interpret.

A group of children are asked to give the month of their birthday. This tally chart shows the data.

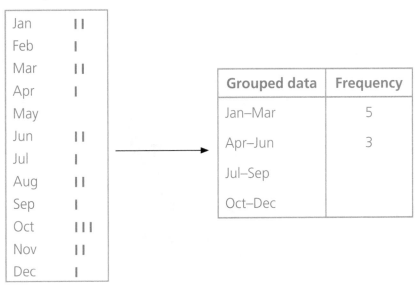

Example

Jan	I I
Feb	I
Mar	I I
Apr	I
May	
Jun	I I
Jul	I
Aug	I I
Sep	I
Oct	I I I
Nov	I I
Dec	I

Grouped data	Frequency
Jan–Mar	5
Apr–Jun	3
Jul–Sep	
Oct–Dec	

Activities

1 Finish the frequency table for the data above.

2 The list below shows the ages of some people in a room.
Complete the frequency table to show the information using grouped data.

84	16
27	30
35	46
45	21
15	9
64	42
37	51
29	91
72	32
44	8

Age	Tally	Frequency
0–29		
30–59		
60–89		
90+		

3 Which age group has the most people? _____

4 How many more **30–59** year olds are there than **60–89** year olds? _____

5 How many fewer **0–29** year olds are there than **30–59** year olds? _____

Drawing bar line charts

Explanation

Bar line charts are sometimes called **bar line graphs**. They are like bar charts but they use lines instead of bars to show amounts.

Example

These two charts show the same information.

The birthday months of a group of 11 year olds

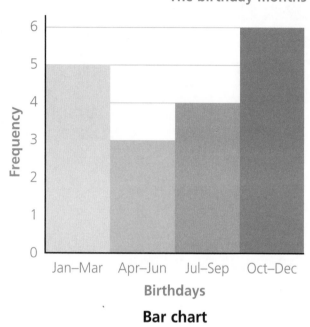

Birthdays

Bar chart

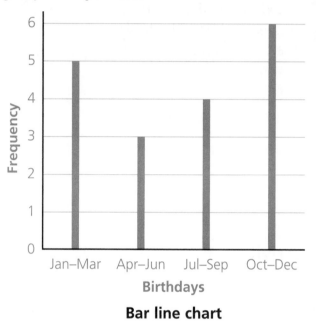

Birthdays

Bar line chart

Activities

1   Draw a bar line chart using the data in this frequency table.

Type of food	Number of grams of fat per 100g
cheese	28
ice cream	20
cookies	31
crisps	33
baked beans	1
yoghurt	5

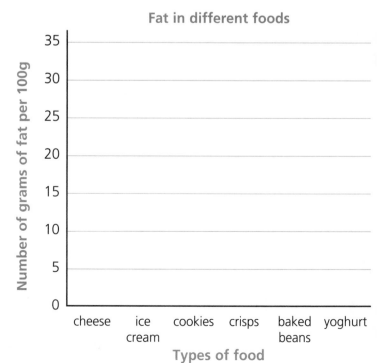

Fat in different foods

Interpreting bar line charts

This bar line chart shows the position of Stalybridge Celtic football team during the last **10** weeks of the season.

Activities

1 In which position was Stalybridge Celtic on:

   a 11 March? _____   **b 22** April? _____   **c 13** May? _____

2 On which date was Stalybridge Celtic in:

   a 12th position? _____   **b 7**th position? _____

3 On which dates was Stalybridge Celtic in **9**th position? _____

4 By how many positions did the team fall between **11** and **25** March? _____

5 By how many positions did the team rise between **8** April and **13** May? _____

6 For how many weeks was the team above **10**th position? _____

Progress test 2

1 The bar chart shows the number of birds that visited the school bird table in one week.
Answer these questions.

    a How many birds visited the table on:

       Monday? _____   Friday? _____

    b On which day were there 20 visitors?

    _____

    c How many birds visited
the table during the week? _____

    d Why might more birds have visited
on Monday?

    _____

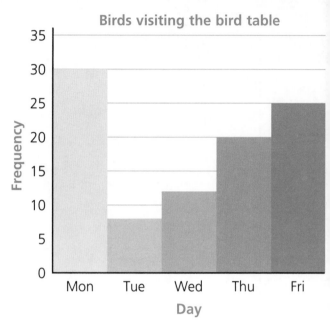

2 Sort the numbers **1–20** using a Venn
diagram labelled **Multiples of 3**
and **Even numbers**

3 This bar line chart shows the number of pupils who were absent from school last term.

    a How many pupils were absent in:

       week **3**?   _____

       week **7**?   _____

    b In which week were
no pupils absent?   _____

    c How many more pupils
were absent in week **8**
than in week **3**?   _____

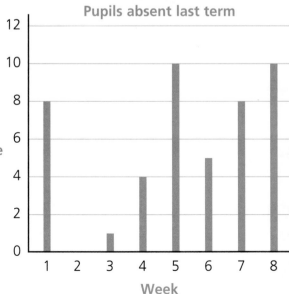

Range and mode

Range

The **range** of a group of numbers is **the difference between the lowest and highest numbers**.

Here is a list of Hannah's recent test scores: **8, 7, 9, 4, 7, 15, 8, 3**

To find the range, find the highest number and subtract the lowest number from it.
So the range is **15 – 3 = 12**.

Activities

1 Find the range of these sets of numbers.

a 5, 17, 12, 21, 8, 16, 8 _____   **b** 6, 9, 29, 34, 11, 17, 28, 36, 40, 8 _____

c 12°C, 36°C, 57°C, 84°C _____   **d** 150kg, 190kg, 42kg, 8kg, 78kg _____

Mode

An average is used to give an idea of a whole set of numbers.

The **mode** is a type of average. It is the **most common**, or most popular, number in a set of data.

In this list of prices, the mode is **16p**, because **16p** occurs **most often**.

$$9p, 16p, 27p, 9p, 5p, 16p, 39p, 16p, 27p$$

Sometimes, like in this set of numbers, there is more than one mode:

$$8, 6, 7, 2, 1, 7, 6, 5, 9, 7, 2, 6$$

The modes of this set of numbers are **6** and **7**, because **6** and **7** both occur three times.

2 Find the mode of these sets of numbers.

a 6, 2, 4, 3, 9, 8, 8, 4, 5, 7, 4, 4, 8   mode _____

b 19, 23, 7, 18, 19, 23, 45, 6, 27, 42, 19   mode _____

c

Shoes available in these sizes
6, 8, 3, 5, 5, 5, 4, 8, 9, 2, 3, 5, 8, 10, 10, 3, 8, 4, 2, 8, 6, 6, 6

d

Goals scored by United this year
1, 0, 2, 6, 3, 1, 0, 3, 6, 2, 4, 4, 1, 2, 5, 0, 0, 2, 2, 1, 4, 1, 3, 6, 3, 5

mode _____   modes _____

Median

Explanation

The **median** is another type of average.

It is the **middle number**, when all the numbers are put in order.

Example
Look at this set of numbers: 9,   7,   2,   10,   2

To find the median put all the numbers in order, like this,

and then find the middle number. So the median is **7**.

2   2   ⑦   9   10
▲
middle number

In this set,   **9,   8,   7,   10,   7**   the median is 8.

7   7   ⑧   9   10
▲
middle number

Activities

1   Find the median of these sets of numbers.

a   3, 7, 9, 2, 4 _____

b   1, 8, 1, 5, 6 _____

c   6, 1, 4, 9, 3, 9, 5 _____

d   2, 10, 10, 10, 3, 4, 10 _____

When there is an even number of numbers in the set, and so there is no middle number, the median is **halfway between the two middle numbers**.

Example
Look at this set of numbers: 2   3   ⑤   ⑥   8   9   The median is $5\frac{1}{2}$.
▲   ▲
middle numbers

Notice that the median number doesn't have to be in the set of data you started with.

---

2   Find the median of these sets of numbers.

a   1, 4, 1, 2, 6, 9, 9, 9 _____

b   3, 5, 6, 2, 9, 3, 5, 7, 2, 1 _____

c   11, 34, 26, 45, 52, 12 _____

d   4, 12, 16, 17, 4, 6, 7, 10, 4, 1 _____

e   33, 45, 14, 56, 24, 37 _____

f   15, 27, 18, 39, 44, 51, 22, 42 _____

Mean

The **mean** is another kind of average.

To find the mean find the **total** of all the values and then **divide** this by the **number of values**.

Example
To find the mean of **10**, **2**, **7**, **9** and **2**:

- add them together $10 + 2 + 7 + 9 + 2 = 30$
- divide by the number of values $30 \div 5\ values = 6$ so the mean is **6**.

To find the mean of this set of numbers   **8, 6, 2, 9, 3, 1, 5, 2**:

- add them together $8 + 6 + 2 + 9 + 3 + 1 + 5 + 2 = 36$
- divide by **8** $36 \div 8 = 4\frac{1}{2}$ so the mean is $4\frac{1}{2}$.

Activities

1 Find the mean of these sets of numbers.

a 3, 6, 1, 5, 2, 7   _____   b 6, 8, 2, 1, 8, 3, 7   _____

c 3, 5, 7, 2, 1, 9, 6, 7   _____   d 10, 4, 2, 7, 1, 1, 8, 3, 4, 10   _____

e 13, 21, 34, 16, 16   _____   f 9, 24, 17, 13, 18, 5, 21, 9   _____

If you know the mean of a set of numbers, you can work out the total of all the numbers by multiplying the mean by the number of values.

Example If the mean of **5** numbers is **4**, then the total of the numbers is **5 × 4 = 20**.

---

2 The mean of these cards is **6**. What is the missing number?

| 6 | 8 | 2 | 7 | |

3 The mean of these cards is **7**. What is the missing number?

| 4 | 8 | 6 | 9 | 9 | |

Mean, median and mode

Explanation

In the previous few pages you learnt about the different averages – mode, median and mean. The averages may be different for the same set of data.

Example Here the mode of these **9** numbers is **2**, the median is **3** and the mean is **5**.

1   2   2   2   3   6   8   9   12

Activities

1   Find the mean, median and mode of these sets of numbers.

a 9, 9, 4, 1, 2, 9, 9, 1, 1

mean _____

median _____

mode _____

b 5, 2, 4, 7, 6, 9, 6, 9

mean _____

median _____

modes _____

c 3, 4, 0, 6, 4, 7, 3, 5, 4

mean _____

median _____

mode _____

d 3, 6, 6, 6, 24

mean _____

median _____

mode _____

It is sometimes more sensible to use one type of average than another. If the owner of a shoe shop has a list of which adult shoe sizes have been sold, it seems unhelpful to use the mean as the average since it might be a decimal such as **4.7**. This would not help the owner to decide which shoe sizes to order more of. In this case the mode would be much more sensible to use.

2   Sanjit describes the average number of sails these boats have using the mode and the mean. Which do you think is more sensible? _____

3   Sanjit describes the average distance travelled by **20** boats in a day. Which average do you think is most sensible to use? _____

Estimating points on a scale

Explanation

On page 12 you learnt the importance of reading scales on axes carefully. Sometimes we must estimate the value of points between marked lines.

Example

This scale is numbered in **10**s.

To work out the value for the **blue** cross, look at the two numbered lines either side of it and estimate its value.

Here its value is **15**. The value for the **grey** cross is **33**.

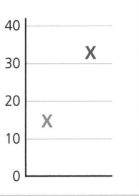

Activities

1   Estimate the value for each cross marked on these scales.

a
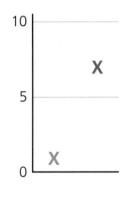

_____ _____

b
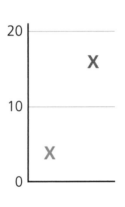

_____ _____

c
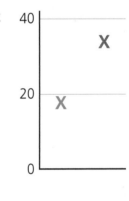

_____ _____

d
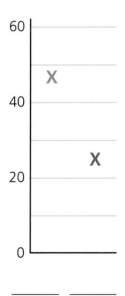

_____ _____

e
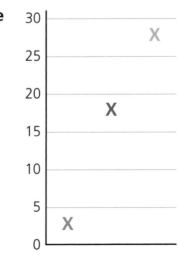

_____ _____ _____

f
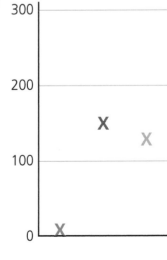

_____ _____ _____

Drawing line graphs

Explanation

Line graphs use lines to join up points on a graph. They are used with data like mass or temperature and often show what is happening over a period of time. Time is always shown along the horizontal axis. Data is plotted and the points are joined together to make a line.

Example

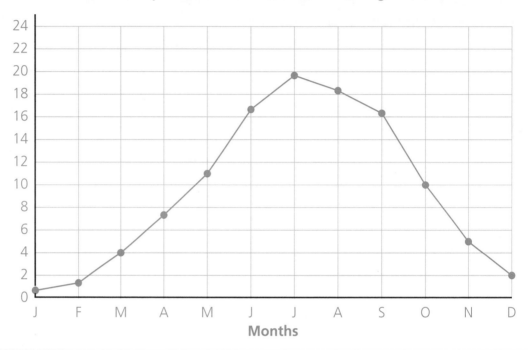

The temperature for each month in Darlingfield in °C

Activities

1   Draw a line graph using the data in this table. It shows the number of times Sarah's heart was beating in one minute at ten-minute intervals.

Time of day (a.m.)	Heart rate per minute
9.00	70
9.10	70
9.20	100
9.30	125
9.40	140
9.50	115
10.00	80

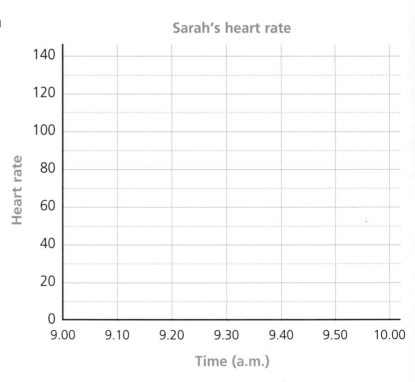

Sarah's heart rate

Interpreting line graphs

Explanation

Here is some information about a helicopter flight during an afternoon.

Time	13:00	13:10	13:20	13:30	13:40	13:50	14:00	14:10
Helicopter's height (m)	0	250	400	500	550	400	150	0

Example

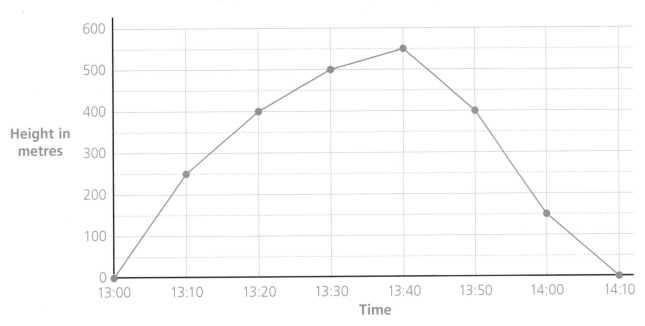

A line graph to show a helicopter's height above the ground

Activities

1 At what time did the helicopter first rise to:

   a 400m? _____   **b** 550m? _____

2 On its descent, when did the helicopter drop to:

   a 400m? _____   **b** 150m? _____

3 At about what times do you think the helicopter was at:

   a 50m? _____ and _____   **b** 275m? _____ and _____

4 Could the helicopter have gone any higher than 550m during its flight? Why do you think this?

   _____

   _____

Progress test 3

1 Draw a line graph using the data in this table. It shows the number of votes Ali has at times during one hour of a radio phone-in.

Time of day (p.m.)	Number of votes in thousands
9.00	10
9.10	20
9.20	35
9.30	50
9.40	80
9.50	95
10.00	100

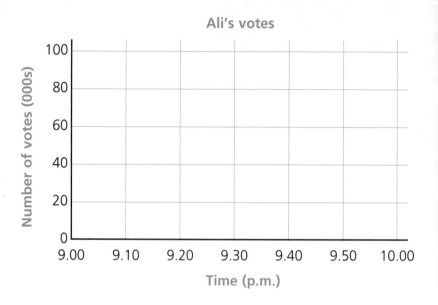

2 Estimate how many thousand people had voted for Ali at these times.

a 9.05 _____

b 9.35 _____

3 In which ten-minute period did most people vote for Ali? _____

4 Find the range of these sets of numbers.

a 15, 37, 25, 26, 2, 36, 38   _____

b 240, 360, 210, 290, 410, 350, 110   _____

5 Find the mode of these sets of numbers.

a 7, 3, 9, 3, 9, 6, 8, 4, 2, 7, 4, 3, 6   mode _____

b 41, 41, 6, 7, 21, 6, 21, 6, 21, 41, 21   mode _____

6 Find the median of these sets of numbers.

a 3, 5, 1, 7, 8, 6, 2 _____   b 5, 10, 9, 9, 4, 7, 5, 1 _____

Statistics

Timetables

Timetables often show the times that buses or trains stop at points along a route. Times are given in either the **12-hour** or **24-hour** clock.

24-hour time

| 0 | 1 | 2 | 3 | 4 | 5 | 6 | 7 | 8 | 9 | 10 | 11 | 12 | 13 | 14 | 15 | 16 | 17 | 18 | 19 | 20 | 21 | 22 | 23 |

a.m.   p.m.

| 12 | 1 | 2 | 3 | 4 | 5 | 6 | 7 | 8 | 9 | 10 | 11 | 12 | 1 | 2 | 3 | 4 | 5 | 6 | 7 | 8 | 9 | 10 | 11 |

12-hour time

If the **24**-hour clock is used, remember that after midday the numbers **13** to **23** are used for the hours.

Example 5.00 p.m. is **17:00**

This is part of a bus timetable from Newcastle to Sunderland.

Monday to Friday						
Newcastle Monument	11:20	11:35	11:50	12:05	12:20	12:35
Gateshead Metro	11:30	11:45	12:00	12:15	12:30	12:45
Queen Elizabeth Hospital	11:40	11:55	12:10	12:25	12:40	12:55
Springwell Village	11:50	12:05	12:20	12:35	12:50	13:05
Donwell	11:55	12:10	12:25	12:40	12:55	13:10
Concord Bus Station	11:59	12:14	12:29	12:44	12:59	13:14
Nissan Factory	12:09	12:24	12:39	12:54	13:09	13:24
Southwick	12:19	12:34	12:49	13:04	13:19	13:34
Sunderland Interchange	12:32	12:47	13:02	13:17	13:32	13:47

Activities

1 How long does it take to get from:

    a Newcastle Monument to Gateshead Metro? _____

    b Newcastle Monument to Springwell Village? _____

    c Queen Elizabeth Hospital to Donwell? _____

    d Concord Bus Station to the Nissan Factory? _____

    e the Nissan Factory to Southwick? _____

    f Southwick to Sunderland Interchange? _____

2 Keira left Donwell at **12:40**. What time did she get to Southwick? _____

3 Jack left Gateshead Metro at **12:30**. When did he get to Donwell? _____

Distance charts

Explanation

Distance charts show distances between places and are read by reading down and across from the places concerned.

Example

You can use this chart to find the distance between Dover and Aberdeen. Point to both place names and come down from the left-hand name and across from the right-hand name until they meet to find the distance. It is **702**km. Similarly the distance from Bristol to London is **160**km.

Aberdeen				
630	Bristol			
702	275	Dover		
405	230	355	Manchester	
641	160	117	263	London

(Distances in kilometres)

Activities

1   Find the distance in kilometres from:

   a Aberdeen to Manchester _____

   b London to Dover _____

   c Manchester to Bristol _____

   d Dover to Bristol _____

When finding distances from one place to another via a particular place, be careful to split the journey into two stages. Find both distances from the chart and add them.

Example

First stage: Aberdeen to Manchester

Second stage: Manchester to Dover

2   Find the distance in kilometres from:

   a Aberdeen to Dover via Manchester _____ + _____ = _____

   b Bristol to Dover via London _____

   c London to Aberdeen via Manchester _____

Statistics

Conversions 1

Explanation

Converting using multiplication and division

There are two main ways of converting between units and you will look at each of them in these next two pages.

The first way involves multiplication and division.

Example

Imagine you are going on holiday and need to convert money into Euros.

Find the exchange rate, which will look like this: £1 = €1.4
This means that, for every £1, you get €1.4.

To convert a number of pounds to another currency, just **multiply** by the exchange rate.

To convert £8 to Euros just multiply £8 by 1.4.

You can use a calculator, but don't forget to always put **two** numbers after the point in money.

£8 ⟶ 8 × 1.4 = 11.2 ⟶ €11.20

Activities

1   Using the above exchange rate convert:

   a   £9 to Euros _____   **b**   £12 to Euros _____

   c   £15 to Euros _____   **d**   £18 to Euros _____

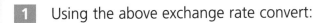

To convert another currency to pounds, just divide by the exchange rate (£1 = €1.4).

Example
To convert **17.50** Euros to pounds just divide by **1.4**.

€17.50 ⟶ 17.5 ÷ 1.4 = 12.5 ⟶ £12.50

2   Using the above exchange rate convert:

   a   8.4 Euros to pounds _____   **b**   15.40 Euros to pounds _____

   c   26.6 Euros to pounds _____   **d**   35 Euros to pounds _____

3   The exchange rate changes to **£1 = €1.3**. Convert:

   a   £17 to Euros _____   **b**   £21 to Euros _____

   c   24.7 Euros to pounds _____   **d**   45.5 Euros to pounds _____

Conversions 2

Explanation

Converting using a conversion graph

You can convert between units by using a **conversion graph** to get a good estimate.

Example

This conversion graph has a straight line that shows the relationship between pounds and Euros.

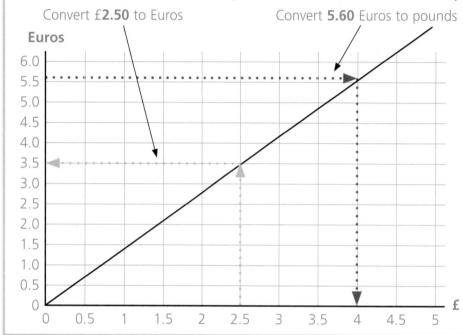

Read up and across to convert from pounds.

£2.50 ⟶ **€3.50**

Read across and down to convert from Euros.

€5.60 ⟶ **£4.00**

Activities

1   Use the conversion graph to approximately convert:

   a   **£3** to Euros _____

   b   **£2.80** to Euros _____

   c   **1.5** Euros to pounds _____

   d   **4.6** Euros to pounds _____

This conversion graph converts between miles and kilometres.

1 mile = 1.6km (approximate)

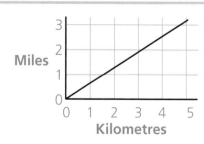

2   Use the conversion graph to approximately convert:

   a   **3** miles to kilometres _____

   b   **1.5** miles to kilometres _____

   c   **2** kilometres to miles _____

   d   **3** kilometres to miles _____

Statistics

Two-way tables

Explanation

Two-way tables are similar to the distance charts you learnt about on page 30. You read information across and down.

Example This table shows the prices of different hotel rooms for one night. Read across from a room type and down from the view to find the price.

		View	
		Sea view	No sea view
Room type	Single (sleeps 1)	£35.75	£33.10
	Double (sleeps 2)	£66.50	£61.45
	Family (sleeps 3)	£78.25	£70.30

Activities

1 How much does it cost for:

a a double room with a sea view? _____

b a family room with no sea view? _____

2 How much more does it cost for a single room with a sea view than a single room with no sea view? _____

A survey asked some people whether they were right- or left-handed. The results are shown here. For some two-way tables, totals can be found to give further information.

The blue boxes can be filled in with the total of each row and column. The total number of all the people surveyed is also shown (**121**).

Example

	Left	Right	
Female	7	46	
Male	5	63	
			121

3 Fill in the **blue** boxes with the totals of each row and column.

4 How many of the people surveyed were:

a left-handed females? _____   **b** right-handed males? _____

c left-handed? _____   **d** males? _____

Interpreting pie charts 1

Explanation

A **pie chart** shows information as different sized portions of a circle.

Example
This pie chart shows how Caitlin spent her free time last Saturday.

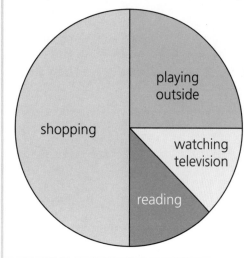

The whole circle shows the whole of Caitlin's free time. The larger each piece of pie (or sector) is, the more time was spent doing it.

Caitlin spent: half of her time shopping
a quarter playing outside
about one-eighth watching television
about one-eighth reading

If Caitlin had **8** hours of free time, the pie chart shows she spent:

4 hours shopping	2 hours playing outside
1 hour reading	1 hour watching television

Activities

1 Look at this pie chart. About what fraction of his free time did Adam spend on each activity?

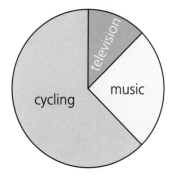

a listening to music _____

b cycling _____

c watching television _____

2 If Adam had **4** hours of free time, about how long did he spend on each activity?

a listening to music _____   **b** cycling _____   **c** watching television _____

3 This pie chart shows where **24** people went on holiday.

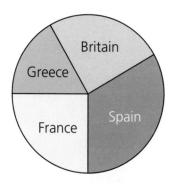

About what **fraction** of the people went to:

a France? _____   **b** Spain? _____

About **how many** spent their holiday in:

c Britain? _____   **d** Greece? _____

Interpreting pie charts 2

Explanation

The pie charts on page 34 involved easy fractions of the whole, such as finding a half, quarter or third of the total number of things being represented. Sometimes it is necessary to use a protractor to measure angles in order to find more difficult fractions of pie charts.

Example

This pie chart shows how Farmer Jackson uses his 200 acres of land.

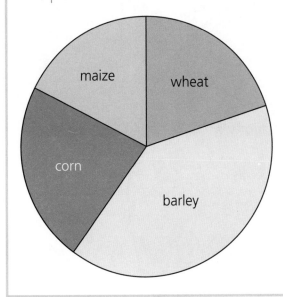

You can use a protractor to measure each angle of this pie chart. When the angle for a sector (slice) is known you can find the number of acres it represents.

The wheat sector is **72°**, so it stands for $\frac{72}{360}$ of the whole. Multiply the fraction by the total number of acres.

$$\frac{72}{360} \times \mathbf{200} = \mathbf{40} \text{ acres}$$

So, first measure the angle, then divide by **360** and finally multiply by the total number of people or items (such as acres).

Activities

1   Measure the angle for:

    a   barley _____   **b**   corn _____   **c**   maize _____

2   Write what fraction of the whole pie is:

    a   barley   **b**   corn   **c**   maize

3   Now find how many acres of the land is:

    a   barley _____   **b**   corn _____   **c**   maize _____

4   Check that the total number of acres of wheat (**40** acres), barley, corn and maize is **200** acres.

Interpreting pie charts 3

Explanation

Remember to check what total number of items or people a pie chart represents.

Example This pie chart shows the results of a survey of **1200** people who were asked to state their favourite sport.

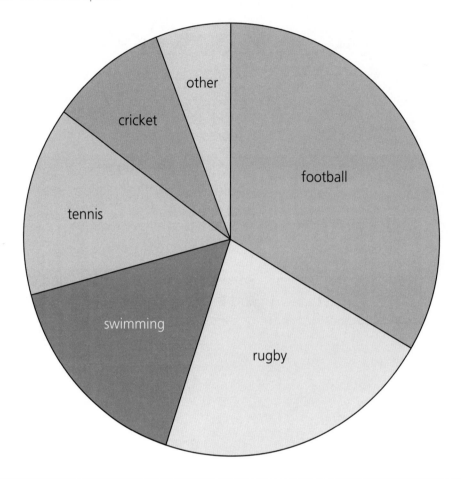

Activities

1. Find how many people chose each of the following.

   a football _____   **b** rugby _____   **c** cricket _____

2. How many more people chose football than cricket? _____

3. How many fewer people chose tennis than rugby? _____

4. How many people altogether chose swimming, tennis or cricket? _____

5. Is it true to say that exactly a quarter of the people chose swimming or cricket? _____

Drawing pie charts

Explanation

To draw pie charts you must find what angle the sector (slice) for each category will be. To find the angle for each sector, divide **360°** by the total number of people or items that the pie chart will represent and then multiply the answer by how many are in each category.

Angle for **one** item = **360°** ÷ the total number of things represented

Example
This table shows the activities or items that **100** boys spend the largest part of their pocket money on.

Activity or item	Number of boys
sports and hobbies	45
clothes	5
music, videos, films	10
computer games	25
other	15

First find the total number of boys represented. Here it is **100**. Then divide **360°** by that number to show the angle for each boy. **360° ÷ 100 = 3.6°**

Finally multiply this angle by the number of boys in each category.

Sports and hobbies   **3.6 × 45 = 162°**

Clothes   **3.6 × 5 = 18°**

Activities

1   Using the table above, find the angle of the pie chart that will be:

   a music, video and films   _____

   b computer games   _____

   c other   _____

2   Check that the five angles have a total of **360°**.

3   Now use a protractor to complete the pie chart.

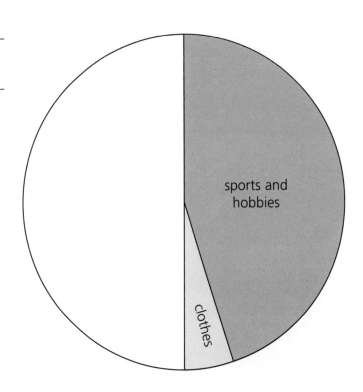

Progress test 4

1 Find the distance in miles from:

   a Aberdeen to Manchester   _____

   b London to Dover   _____

   c London to Aberdeen via Manchester   _____

Aberdeen				
394	**Bristol**			
439	172	**Dover**		
253	144	222	**Manchester**	
401	100	73	164	**London**

Distances in miles

2 How many of the people surveyed were:

	Vegetarian?		
	Yes	No	
Female	48	73	
Male	62	17	

   a female vegetarians?   _____

   b males who are not vegetarian?   _____

   c males?   _____

   d vegetarian?   _____

   e How many people were
       surveyed altogether?   _____

3 This pie chart shows what **48** people ate for tea.

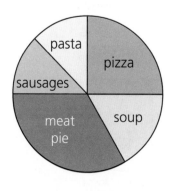

About what **fraction** of the people ate:

   a pizza?   _____   **b** meat pie? _____

About **how many** people ate:

   c sausages? _____   **d** soup?   _____

Misleading statistics

Explanation

Sometimes graphs and charts can be misleading. The same information can be presented in different ways to show a different point of view.

Example
Look at this data which shows the number of people who are unemployed.

Unemployment (to the nearest thousand)

Year	2012	2013	2014
Number of unemployed	1 200 000	1 203 000	1 210 000

Here are two graphs showing this information.

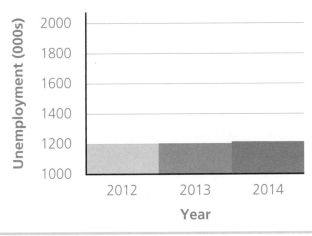
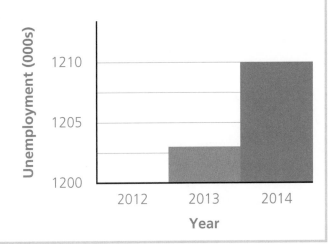

Activities

1   Look carefully at the scale on each graph. For the left-hand graph:

   a Which number does the scale start at? _____

   b What size steps does the scale go up in? _____

   c Does the number of people unemployed look stable from year to year? _____

2   For the right-hand graph:

   a Which number does the scale start at? _____

   b What size steps does the scale go up in? _____

   c Does the number of people unemployed look stable from year to year? _____

3   Write in your own words why you think the two graphs look so different.

_____

_____

Scatter graphs

Explanation

Scatter graphs show whether there is a connection between two sets of values, for example, whether there is a connection between people's heights and the length of their leg.

Example This scatter graph shows that the longer the person's leg, the greater their height is.

A scatter graph could show:
- that one value increases as the other increases
- that one value increases as the other decreases
- no connection at all.

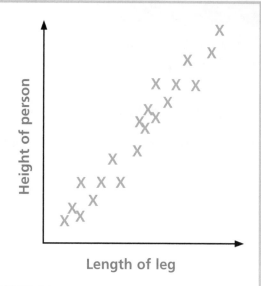

Activities

1   Draw a scatter graph to show the number of cold drinks sold per hour by a seaside shop according to the outside temperature.

Temperature °C	0	4	8	12	16	20	24	28	32	36
Number of cold drinks sold each hour	1	3	6	11	19	28	35	41	48	58

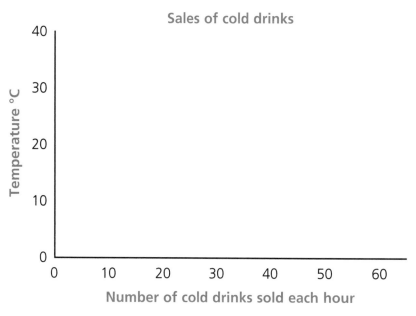

2   Do the dots on each scatter graph form a pattern? _____

3   Tick which is the true statement.

☐ The higher the temperature the fewer drinks were sold.

☐ The higher the temperature the more drinks were sold.

Final test

1 Draw a line graph using the data in this table. It shows the number of telephone votes Kazuko received during two hours of a television dance competition.

Time of day (p.m.)	Number of votes in thousands
7.00	10
7.20	30
7.40	45
8.00	55
8.20	70
8.40	95
9.00	100

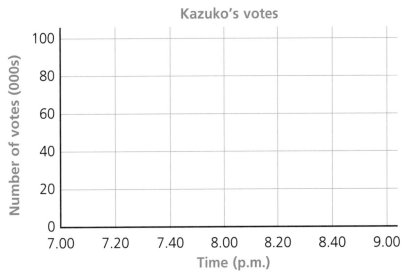

Kazuko's votes

2 Count the shapes, make a frequency table of the data, and answer the questions.

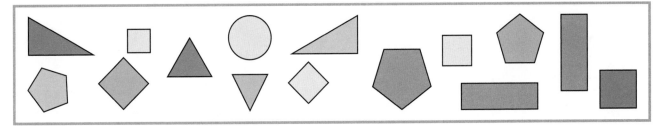

Shape	Tally	Number
triangles		
squares		
rectangles		
circles		
pentagons		

a How many squares are there? _____

b Of which shape are there two? _____

c Which two shapes together have a total of **8**?

_____ and _____

d How many shapes are there altogether? _____

3 This bar chart shows the number of cans in a drinks machine during one day.

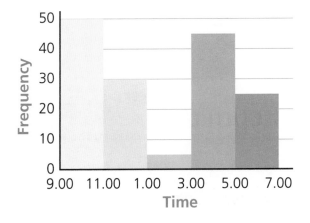

a About how many cans were sold between:

9.00 and **11.00**? _____

11.00 and **1.00**? _____

b During which period were **25** cans sold?

between _____ and _____

c Estimate the total number of cans sold between

9.00 a.m. and **7.00** p.m. _____

4 Sort these names using this Carroll diagram.

	Daniel
	Megan
	Lucy
	Alice
	Ananya
	Hannah
	Leah
	Mark

	Names that start with M	Names that do not start with M
Names that have four letters		
Names that do not have four letters		

5 Find the mean, median and mode of these sets of numbers.

a 7, 6, 4, 1, 3, 6, 1, 7, 1

mean _____

median _____

mode _____

b 8, 5, 7, 10, 9, 12, 9, 12

mean _____

median _____

modes _____

6 This bar line chart shows the number of pupils who were absent from school last term.

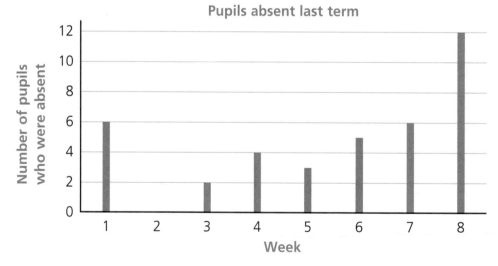

Pupils absent last term

a How many pupils were absent in: week 1? _____   week 5? _____

b In which week were no pupils absent? _____

c How many more pupils were absent in week 8 than week 4? _____

d Why might so many pupils have been absent in week 8? _____

Statistics

7 Draw a line graph using the data in this table. It shows the number of votes given to Mia during one hour of a 'Pop Star' phone-in.

Time of day (p.m.)	Number of votes in thousands
9.00	10
9.10	20
9.20	35
9.30	50
9.40	80
9.50	95
10.00	100

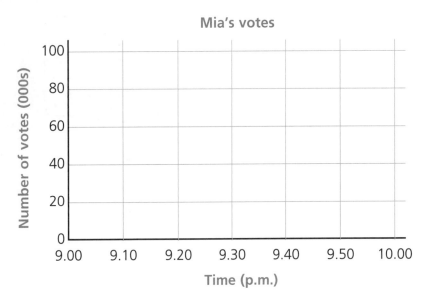

8 This conversion graph converts between litres and gallons.

4.5 litres = **1** gallon (approximate)

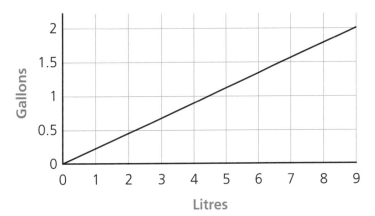

Use the conversion graph to approximately convert:

a 0.5 gallons to litres _____

b 1.2 gallons to litres _____

c 9 litres to gallons _____

d 3 litres to gallons _____

9 This pie chart shows what **60** people ate for dinner.

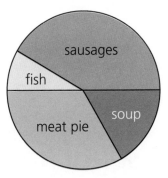

About what **fraction** of the people ate:

a sausages? _____

b fish? _____

About **how many** people ate:

c meat pie? _____

d soup? _____

This pie chart shows the favourite colour of 150 people.

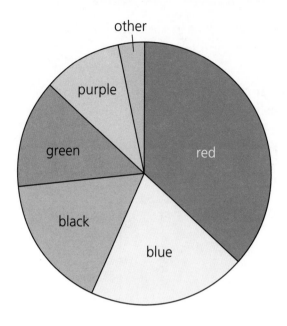

10 Find how many people chose:

a red _____

b blue _____

c purple _____

11 How many more people chose black than purple? _____

12 How many fewer people chose green than red? _____

13 This table shows the activities or items that **100** girls spend the largest part of their pocket money on.

Draw a pie chart to show the information in the table.

Activity or item	Number of girls
clothes	50
music, videos, films	25
sports and hobbies	10
other	10
computer games	5

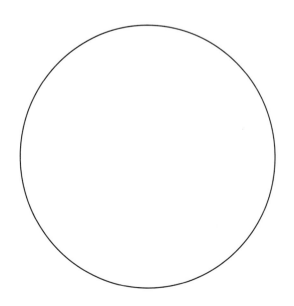

Answers to Activities

Page 4: Lists

1 your own lists

2 10, 12, 14, 16, 18, 20, 22, 24

Page 5: Pictograms 1

1

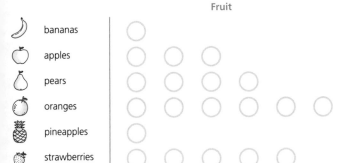

Fruit

bananas
apples
pears
oranges
pineapples
strawberries

Page 6: Pictograms 2

1 **a** 5

b 15

c 1

d 20

2

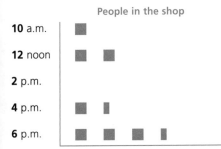

People in the shop

10 a.m.
12 noon
2 p.m.
4 p.m.
6 p.m.

Page 7: Frequency tables

1

Pet	Number
hamsters	5
dogs	3
cats	4
rabbits	2
budgies	3

a 3
b rabbits
c cats and hamsters
d 17
e 1

Page 8: Tallying

1 & **2** experiment results

Page 9: Drawing bar charts 1

1

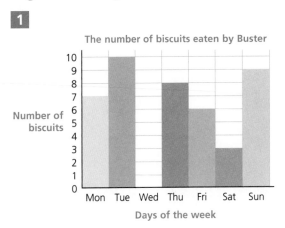

The number of biscuits eaten by Buster

Page 10: Drawing bar charts 2

1

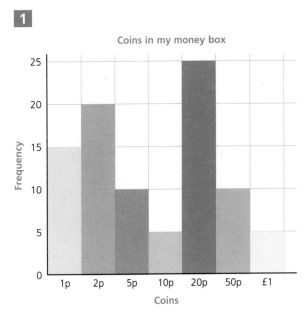

Coins in my money box

2

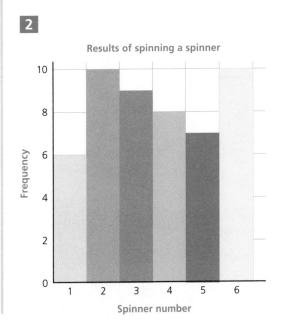

Results of spinning a spinner

Page 12: Reading scales

1
a 1, 8
b 2, 14
c 30, 90
d 80, 140
e 5, 35, 50
f 25, 250, 175

Page 13: Interpreting bar charts 1

1 approximately: **a** 80   **b** 70   **c** 125

2 approximately: **a** 100   **b** 20   **c** 130

3 Wednesday

4 library closed for example

5 more free time at the weekend

6 Tuesday

Page 14: Venn diagrams

1

Numbers with 4 tens   Odd numbers

40   47   27

44   35

48   41   25   19

26
14
30

Page 15: Carroll diagrams

1

	Odd	Not odd
Numbers that have four 10s	41 47	40 44 48
Numbers that do not have four 10s	27 35 19 25	30 26 14

Page 16: Interpreting bar charts 2

1
a 7
b 14
c 10
d 15
e 11

2
a 7
b 3

3 25

4 57

Page 17: Grouped data

1 4, 6

2

Age	Tally	Frequency
0–29	⊞⊞ II	7
30–59	⊞⊞ IIII	9
60–89	III	3
90+	I	1

3 30–59

4 6

5 2

Page 18: Drawing bar line charts

1

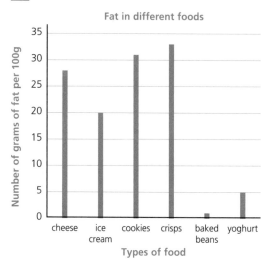

Fat in different foods

Page 19: Interpreting bar line charts

1 **a** 9th   **b** 7th   **c** 1st

2 **a** 25 March   **b** 22 April

3 11 March, 1 April, 15 April

4 3

5 10

6 7 weeks

Page 21: Range and mode

1 **a** 16   **b** 34   **c** 72°C   **d** 182kg

2 **a** 4   **b** 19   **c** 8   **d** 1 and 2

Page 22: Median

1 **a** 4   **b** 5
    c 5   **d** 10

2 **a** 5   **b** 4
    c 30   **d** $6\frac{1}{2}$
    e 35   **f** 33

Page 23: Mean

1 **a** 4   **b** 5
    c 5   **d** 5
    e 20   **f** $14\frac{1}{2}$

2 7

3 6

Page 24: Mean, median and mode

1 **a** mean 5, median 4, mode 9
    b mean 6, median 6, modes 6 and 9
    c mean 4, median 4, mode 4
    d mean 9, median 6, mode 6

2 mode

3 mean

Page 25: Estimating points on a scale

1 approximately:
    a 1, 7
    b 4, 16
    c 18, 34
    d 47, 25
    e 3, 18, 28
    f 10, 150, 130

Page 26: Drawing line graphs

1

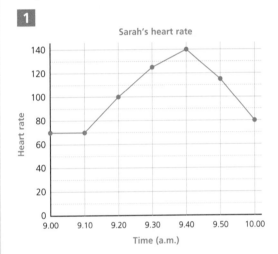

Sarah's heart rate

Page 27: Interpreting line graphs

1 **a** 13:20   **b** 13:40

2 **a** 13:50   **b** 14:00

3 **a** 13:02 and 14:06
    b 13:12 and 13:55

4 Yes, as the graph only shows the height of the helicopter at particular times, not at all the times in between.

Page 29: Timetables

1 **a** 10 minutes
    b 30 minutes
    c 15 minutes
    d 10 minutes
    e 10 minutes
    f 13 minutes

2 13:04

3 12:55

Page 30: Distance charts

1 **a** 405km   **b** 117km
   c 230km   **d** 275km

2 **a** 760km
   b 277km
   c 668km

Page 31: Conversions 1

1 **a** €12.60   **b** €16.80
   c €21   **d** €25.20

2 **a** £6   **b** £11
   c £19   **d** £25

3 **a** €22.10   **b** €27.30
   c £19   **d** £35

Page 32: Conversions 2

1 approximately:
   a €4.20   **b** €4.00
   c £1.07   **d** £3.30

2 approximately:
   a 4.8km   **b** 2.4km
   c 1.25 miles   **d** 1.8 miles

Page 33: Two-way tables

1 **a** £66.50
   b £70.30

2 £2.65

3

	Left	Right	
Female	7	46	53
Male	5	63	68
	12	109	121

4 **a** 7   **b** 63   **c** 12   **d** 68

Page 34: Interpreting pie charts 1

1 approximately:
   a $\frac{1}{4}$ **b** $\frac{5}{8}$ **c** $\frac{1}{8}$

2 **a** 1 hour   **b** $2\frac{1}{2}$ hours   **c** $\frac{1}{2}$ hour

3 approximately:
   a $\frac{1}{4}$ **b** $\frac{1}{3}$ **c** 6   **d** 4

Page 35: Interpreting pie charts 2

1 **a** 144°   **b** 81°   **c** 63°

2 **a** $\frac{144}{360}$ **b** $\frac{81}{360}$ **c** $\frac{63}{360}$

3 **a** 80 acres   **b** 45 acres   **c** 35 acres

4 It is.

Page 36: Interpreting pie charts 3

1 **a** 400   **b** 260   **c** 110

2 290

3 90

4 470

5 yes

Page 37: Drawing pie charts

1 **a** 36°   **b** 90°   **c** 54°

2 They do.

3

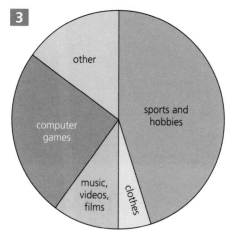

Page 39: Misleading statistics

1 **a** 1000 (000s)

b 200 (000s)

c yes

2 **a** 1200 (000s)

b 5 (000s)

c no

3 Your own comments regarding the difference in scale of the two graphs

Page 40: Scatter graphs

1

2 yes

3 The second statement is true.

Answers to Progress tests

PROGRESS TEST 1 – Page 11

1   10, 15, 20, 25, 30, 35, 40, 45

2   **a**   8

     b   1

     c   Wednesday

     d   19

3

Ride	The number of times I went on	
	Tally	**Frequency**
Twister	III	3
Laser	⊬⊬⊬	5
Cascade	II	2
Screamer	⊬⊬⊬ III	8
Warp	⊬⊬⊬ I	6

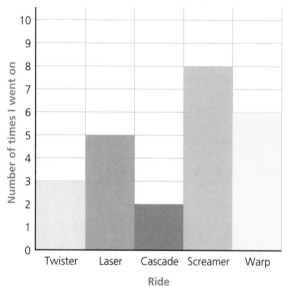

My visit to the theme park

PROGRESS TEST 2 – Page 20

1   **a**   30, 25

     b   Thursday

     c   approximately: 95

     d   Food might have been put out.
        (Accept any plausible answer.)

2

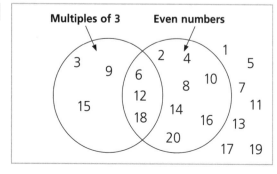

3   **a**   1, 8

     b   week 2

     c   9

PROGRESS TEST 3 – Page 28

1

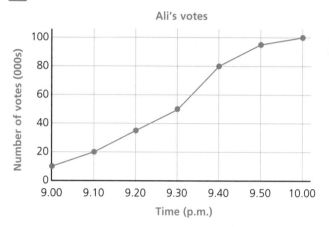

Ali's votes

2   approximately:

     a   15 000   **b**   70 000

3   between 9.30 and 9.40

4   **a**   36

     b   300

5   **a**   3

     b   21

6   **a**   5

     b   6

PROGRESS TEST 4 – Page 38

1   **a**   253 miles

     b   73 miles

     c   417 miles

2   **a**   48   **b**   17   **c**   79   **d**   110   **e**   200

3   approximately:

     a $\frac{1}{4}$ **b** $\frac{1}{3}$ **c**   6   **d**   8

FINAL TEST – Pages 41–44

1

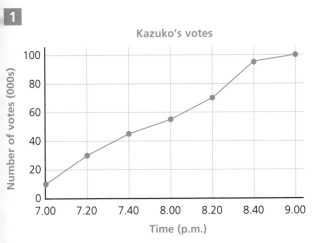

Kazuko's votes

2

Shape	Tally	Number
triangles	IIII	4
squares	HHT	5
rectangles	II	2
circles	I	1
pentagons	III	3

a 5

b rectangles

c squares and pentagons

d 15

3 **a** approximately: 50, 30

b between 5.00 p.m. and 7.00 p.m.

c approximately: 155

4

	Names that start with M	Names that do not start with M
Names that have four letters	Mark	Lucy Leah
Names that do not have four letters	Megan	Daniel Alice Hannah Ananya

5 **a** mean 4, median 4, mode 1

b mean 9, median 9, modes 9 and 12

6 **a** 6, 3

b week 2

c 8

d They might all have caught the same bug.

7

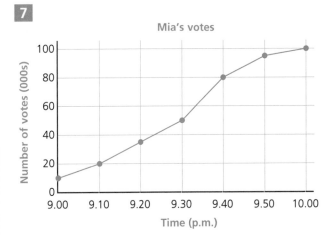

Mia's votes

8 approximately:

a 2.25 litres   **b** 5.4 litres

c 2 gallons   **d** $\frac{2}{3}$ gallon

9 approximately:

a $\frac{5}{12}$ **b** $\frac{1}{12}$

c 20   **d** 10

10 **a** 55   **b** 30   **c** 15

11 35

12 30

13

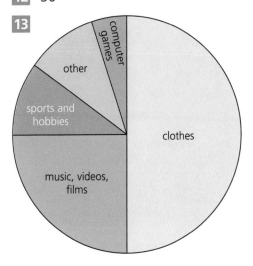